BBC

DOCTOR
WHO

PERSONAL INFORMATION

NAME:

ADDRESS:

PHONE:

E-MAIL:

IN AN EMERGENCY PLEASE CONTACT

NAME:

ADDRESS:

PHONE:

DOCTOR PHONE:

KNOWN ALLERGIES:

JANUARY

M	T	W	T	F	S	S
		1	2	3	4	5
6	7	8	9	10	11	12
13	14	15	16	17	18	19
20	21	22	23	24	25	26
27	28	29	30	31		

FEBRUARY

M	T	W	T	F	S	S
					1	2
3	4	5	6	7	8	9
10	11	12	13	14	15	16
17	18	19	20	21	22	23
24	25	26	27	28	29	

MARCH

M	T	W	T	F	S	S
						1
2	3	4	5	6	7	8
9	10	11	12	13	14	15
16	17	18	19	20	21	22
23	24	25	26	27	28	29
30	31					

APRIL

M	T	W	T	F	S	S
		1	2	3	4	5
6	7	8	9	10	11	12
13	14	15	16	17	18	19
20	21	22	23	24	25	26
27	28	29	30			

MAY

M	T	W	T	F	S	S
				1	2	3
4	5	6	7	8	9	10
11	12	13	14	15	16	17
18	19	20	21	22	23	24
25	26	27	28	29	30	31

JUNE

M	T	W	T	F	S	S
1	2	3	4	5	6	7
8	9	10	11	12	13	14
15	16	17	18	19	20	21
22	23	24	25	26	27	28
29	30					

JULY

M	T	W	T	F	S	S
		1	2	3	4	5
6	7	8	9	10	11	12
13	14	15	16	17	18	19
20	21	22	23	24	25	26
27	28	29	30	31		

AUGUST

M	T	W	T	F	S	S
					1	2
3	4	5	6	7	8	9
10	11	12	13	14	15	16
17	18	19	20	21	22	23
24	25	26	27	28	29	30
31						

SEPTEMBER

M	T	W	T	F	S	S
	1	2	3	4	5	6
7	8	9	10	11	12	13
14	15	16	17	18	19	20
21	22	23	24	25	26	27
28	29	30				

OCTOBER

M	T	W	T	F	S	S
			1	2	3	4
5	6	7	8	9	10	11
12	13	14	15	16	17	18
19	20	21	22	23	24	25
26	27	28	29	30	31	

NOVEMBER

M	T	W	T	F	S	S
						1
2	3	4	5	6	7	8
9	10	11	12	13	14	15
16	17	18	19	20	21	22
23	24	25	26	27	28	29
30						

DECEMBER

M	T	W	T	F	S	S
	1	2	3	4	5	6
7	8	9	10	11	12	13
14	15	16	17	18	19	20
21	22	23	24	25	26	27
28	29	30	31			

JANUARY

M	T	W	T	F	S	S
				1	2	3
4	5	6	7	8	9	10
11	12	13	14	15	16	17
18	19	20	21	22	23	24
25	26	27	28	29	30	31

FEBRUARY

M	T	W	T	F	S	S
1	2	3	4	5	6	7
8	9	10	11	12	13	14
15	16	17	18	19	20	21
22	23	24	25	26	27	28

MARCH

M	T	W	T	F	S	S
1	2	3	4	5	6	7
8	9	10	11	12	13	14
15	16	17	18	19	20	21
22	23	24	25	26	27	28
29	30	31				

APRIL

M	T	W	T	F	S	S
			1	2	3	4
5	6	7	8	9	10	11
12	13	14	15	16	17	18
19	20	21	22	23	24	25
26	27	28	29	30		

MAY

M	T	W	T	F	S	S
					1	2
3	4	5	6	7	8	9
10	11	12	13	14	15	16
17	18	19	20	21	22	23
24	25	26	27	28	29	30
31						

JUNE

M	T	W	T	F	S	S
	1	2	3	4	5	6
7	8	9	10	11	12	13
14	15	16	17	18	19	20
21	22	23	24	25	26	27
28	29	30				

JULY

M	T	W	T	F	S	S
			1	2	3	4
5	6	7	8	9	10	11
12	13	14	15	16	17	18
19	20	21	22	23	24	25
26	27	28	29	30	31	

AUGUST

M	T	W	T	F	S	S
						1
2	3	4	5	6	7	8
9	10	11	12	13	14	15
16	17	18	19	20	21	22
23	24	25	26	27	28	29
30	31					

SEPTEMBER

M	T	W	T	F	S	S
		1	2	3	4	5
6	7	8	9	10	11	12
13	14	15	16	17	18	19
20	21	22	23	24	25	26
27	28	29	30			

OCTOBER

M	T	W	T	F	S	S
				1	2	3
4	5	6	7	8	9	10
11	12	13	14	15	16	17
18	19	20	21	22	23	24
25	26	27	28	29	30	31

NOVEMBER

M	T	W	T	F	S	S
1	2	3	4	5	6	7
8	9	10	11	12	13	14
15	16	17	18	19	20	21
22	23	24	25	26	27	28
29	30					

DECEMBER

M	T	W	T	F	S	S
		1	2	3	4	5
6	7	8	9	10	11	12
13	14	15	16	17	18	19
20	21	22	23	24	25	26
27	28	29	30	31		

NOTABLE DATES

JANUARY

1 NEW YEAR'S DAY

4 BANK HOLIDAY (SCOTLAND)

FEBRUARY

12 CHINESE NEW YEAR (OX)

14 ST. VALENTINE'S DAY

16 SHROVE TUESDAY

MARCH

1 ST. DAVID'S DAY (WALES)

4 WORLD BOOK DAY

14 MOTHERING SUNDAY

17 ST. PATRICK'S DAY

27 PASSOVER BEGINS

28 DAYLIGHT SAVING TIME STARTS

APRIL

2 GOOD FRIDAY (UK)

4 EASTER SUNDAY

5 EASTER MONDAY

12 RAMADAN BEGINS

23 ST. GEORGE'S DAY

MAY

3 EARLY MAY BANK HOLIDAY

31 SPRING BANK HOLIDAY

JUNE

20 FATHER'S DAY

JULY

12 BATTLE OF THE BOYNE (NORTHERN IRELAND)

AUGUST

2 SUMMER BANK HOLIDAY (SCOTLAND)

9 ISLAMIC NEW YEAR BEGINS

30 SUMMER BANK HOLIDAY (ENG, NIR, WAL)

SEPTEMBER

6 ROSH HASHANAH (JEWISH NEW YEAR) BEGINS

15 YOM KIPPUR (DAY OF ATONEMENT) BEGINS

21 THE UNITED NATIONS INTERNATIONAL DAY OF PEACE

OCTOBER

10 WORLD MENTAL HEALTH DAY

31 DAYLIGHT SAVING TIME ENDS

31 HALLOWEEN

NOVEMBER

4 DIWALI

5 GUY FAWKES NIGHT

14 REMEMBRANCE SUNDAY

30 ST. ANDREW'S DAY (SCOTLAND)

DECEMBER

25 CHRISTMAS DAY

26 BOXING DAY

27 BANK HOLIDAY

28 BANK HOLIDAY

31 NEW YEAR'S EVE

PLANNER

JANUARY		FEBRUARY	
1	F	1	M
2	**S**	**2**	**T**
3	**S**	3	W
4	M	4	T
5	T	5	F
6	W	**6**	**S**
7	T	**7**	**S**
8	F	8	M
9	**S**	9	T
10	**S**	10	W
11	M	11	T
12	T	12	F
13	W	**13**	**S**
14	T	**14**	**S**
15	F	15	M
16	**S**	16	T
17	**S**	17	W
18	M	18	T
19	T	19	F
20	W	**20**	**S**
21	T	**21**	**S**
22	F	22	M
23	**S**	23	T
24	**S**	24	W
25	M	25	T
26	T	26	F
27	W	**27**	**S**
28	T	**28**	**S**
29	F		
30	**S**		
31	**S**		

MARCH	APRIL
1 M	1 T
2 T	2 F
3 W	**3 S**
4 T	**4 S**
5 F	5 M
6 S	6 T
7 S	7 W
8 M	8 T
9 T	9 F
10 W	**10 S**
11 T	**11 S**
12 F	12 M
13 S	13 T
14 S	14 W
15 M	15 T
16 T	16 F
17 W	**17 S**
18 T	**18 S**
19 F	19 M
20 S	20 T
21 S	21 W
22 M	22 T
23 T	23 F
24 W	**24 S**
25 T	**25 S**
26 F	26 M
27 S	27 T
28 S	28 W
29 M	29 T
30 T	30 F
31 W	

MAY		JUNE	
1 S		1 T	
2 S		2 W	
3 M		3 T	
4 T		4 F	
5 W		5 S	
6 T		6 S	
7 F		7 M	
8 S		8 T	
9 S		9 W	
10 M		10 T	
11 T		11 F	
12 W		12 S	
13 T		13 S	
14 F		14 M	
15 S		15 T	
16 S		16 W	
17 M		17 T	
18 T		18 F	
19 W		19 S	
20 T		20 S	
21 F		21 M	
22 S		22 T	
23 S		23 W	
24 M		24 T	
25 T		25 F	
26 W		26 S	
27 T		27 S	
28 F		28 M	
29 S		29 T	
30 S		30 W	
31 M			

JULY	AUGUST
1 T	1 S
2 F	2 M
3 S	3 T
4 S	4 W
5 M	5 T
6 T	6 F
7 W	**7 S**
8 T	**8 S**
9 F	9 M
10 S	10 T
11 S	11 W
12 M	12 T
13 T	13 F
14 W	**14 S**
15 T	**15 S**
16 F	16 M
17 S	17 T
18 S	18 W
19 M	19 T
20 T	20 F
21 W	**21 S**
22 T	**22 S**
23 F	23 M
24 S	24 T
25 S	25 W
26 M	26 T
27 T	27 F
28 W	**28 S**
29 T	**29 S**
30 F	30 M
31 S	31 T

SEPTEMBER		OCTOBER	
1 W		1 F	
2 T		**2 S**	
3 F		**3 S**	
4 S		4 M	
5 S		5 T	
6 M		6 W	
7 T		7 T	
8 W		8 F	
9 T		**9 S**	
10 F		**10 S**	
11 S		11 M	
12 S		12 T	
13 M		13 W	
14 T		14 T	
15 W		15 F	
16 T		**16 S**	
17 F		**17 S**	
18 S		18 M	
19 S		19 T	
20 M		20 W	
21 T		21 T	
22 W		22 F	
23 T		**23 S**	
24 F		**24 S**	
25 S		25 M	
26 S		26 T	
27 M		27 W	
28 T		28 T	
29 W		29 F	
30 T		**30 S**	
		31 S	

NOVEMBER		DECEMBER	
1	M	1	W
2	T	2	T
3	W	3	F
4	T	**4**	**S**
5	F	**5**	**S**
6	**S**	6	M
7	**S**	7	T
8	M	8	W
9	T	9	T
10	W	10	F
11	T	**11**	**S**
12	F	**12**	**S**
13	**S**	13	M
14	**S**	14	T
15	M	15	W
16	T	16	T
17	W	17	F
18	T	**18**	**S**
19	F	**19**	**S**
20	**S**	20	M
21	**S**	21	T
22	M	22	W
23	T	23	T
24	W	24	F
25	T	**25**	**S**
26	F	**26**	**S**
27	**S**	27	M
28	**S**	28	T
29	M	29	W
30	T	30	T
		31	F

MON
28

TUE
29

WED
30

THU
31

FRI
1   NEW YEAR'S DAY

SAT
2

SUN
3

MON
4

BANK HOLIDAY (SCOTLAND)

TUE
5

WED
6

THU
7

FRI
8

SAT
9

SUN
10

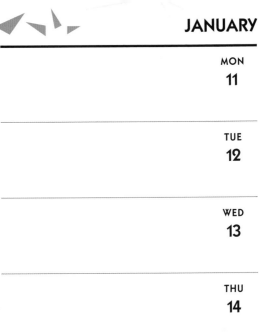

MON
11

TUE
12

WED
13

THU
14

FRI
15

SAT
16

SUN
17

MON
18

TUE
19

WED
20

THU
21

FRI
22

SAT
23

SUN
24

MON
25

TUE
26

WED
27

THU
28

FRI
29

SAT
30

SUN
31

MON
1

TUE
2

WED
3

THU
4

FRI
5

SAT
6

SUN
7

FEBRUARY

MON
8

TUE
9

WED
10

THU
11

FRI
12   CHINESE NEW YEAR (OX)

SAT
13

SUN
14   ST. VALENTINE'S DAY

MON
15

SHROVE TUESDAY

TUE
16

WED
17

THU
18

FRI
19

SAT
20

SUN
21

MON
22

TUE
23

WED
24

THU
25

FRI
26

SAT
27

SUN
28

ST. DAVID'S DAY (WALES)

MON
1

TUE
2

WED
3

WORLD BOOK DAY

THU
4

FRI
5

SAT
6

SUN
7

MARCH

MON
8

TUE
9

WED
10

THU
11

FRI
12

SAT
13

SUN
14   MOTHERING SUNDAY

THE
DOCTOR

MON
15

TUE
16

WED
17

ST. PATRICK'S DAY

THU
18

FRI
19

SAT
20

SUN
21

MON
22

TUE
23

WED
24

THU
25

FRI
26

PASSOVER BEGINS

SAT
27

DAYLIGHT SAVING TIME STARTS

SUN
28

MON
29

TUE
30

WED
31

THU
1

FRI
2   GOOD FRIDAY (UK)

SAT
3

SUN
4   EASTER SUNDAY

MON
5

EASTER MONDAY

TUE
6

WED
7

THU
8

FRI
9

SAT
10

SUN
11

RAMADAN BEGINS

MON
12

TUE
13

WED
14

THU
15

FRI
16

SAT
17

SUN
18

APRIL

MON
19

TUE
20

WED
21

THU
22

FRI
23   ST. GEORGE'S DAY

SAT
24

SUN
25

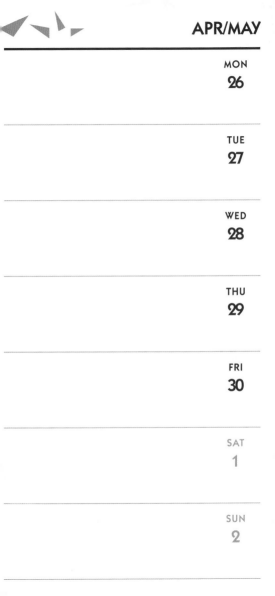

MON
26

TUE
27

WED
28

THU
29

FRI
30

SAT
1

SUN
2

MAY

MON
3   EARLY MAY BANK HOLIDAY

TUE
4

WED
5

THU
6

FRI
7

SAT
8

SUN
9

CALL ME MASTER

MON
10

TUE
11

WED
12

THU
13

FRI
14

SAT
15

SUN
16

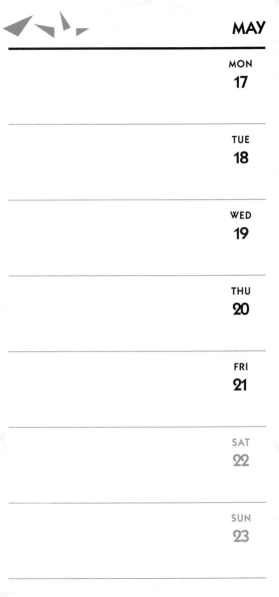

MAY

MON
17

TUE
18

WED
19

THU
20

FRI
21

SAT
22

SUN
23

MON
24

TUE
25

WED
26

THU
27

FRI
28

SAT
29

SUN
30

SPRING BANK HOLIDAY

MON
31

TUE
1

WED
2

THU
3

FRI
4

SAT
5

SUN
6

MON
7

TUE
8

WED
9

THU
10

FRI
11

SAT
12

SUN
13

MON
14

TUE
15

WED
16

THU
17

FRI
18

SAT
19

SUN
20

FATHER'S DAY

MON
21

TUE
22

WED
23

THU
24

FRI
25

SAT
26

SUN
27

MON
28

TUE
29

WED
30

THU
1

FRI
2

SAT
3

SUN
4

JULY

MON
5

TUE
6

WED
7

THU
8

FRI
9

SAT
10

SUN
11

BATTLE OF THE BOYNE (NORTHERN IRELAND)

MON
12

TUE
13

WED
14

THU
15

FRI
16

SAT
17

SUN
18

MON
19

TUE
20

WED
21

THU
22

FRI
23

SAT
24

SUN
25

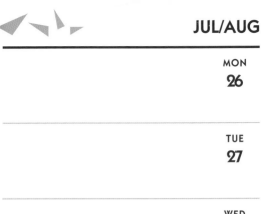

MON
26

TUE
27

WED
28

THU
29

FRI
30

SAT
31

SUN
1

MON
2   SUMMER BANK HOLIDAY (SCOTLAND)

TUE
3

WED
4

THU
5

FRI
6

SAT
7

SUN
8

I'M THE
DOCTOR

AUGUST

MON
9

ISLAMIC NEW YEAR BEGINS

TUE
10

WED
11

THU
12

FRI
13

SAT
14

SUN
15

MON
16

TUE
17

WED
18

THU
19

FRI
20

SAT
21

SUN
22

MON
23

TUE
24

WED
25

THU
26

FRI
27

SAT
28

SUN
29

SUMMER BANK HOLIDAY (ENG, NIR, WAL)

MON
30

TUE
31

WED
1

THU
2

FRI
3

SAT
4

SUN
5

SEPTEMBER

MON
6   ROSH HASHANAH (JEWISH NEW YEAR) BEGINS

TUE
7

WED
8

THU
9

FRI
10

SAT
11

SUN
12

MON
13

TUE
14

WED
15   YOM KIPPUR (DAY OF ATONEMENT) BEGINS

THU
16

FRI
17

SAT
18

SUN
19

MON
20

THE UNITED NATIONS INTERNATIONAL DAY OF PEACE

TUE
21

WED
22

THU
23

FRI
24

SAT
25

SUN
26

MON
27

TUE
28

WED
29

THU
30

FRI
1

SAT
2

SUN
3

MON
4

TUE
5

WED
6

THU
7

FRI
8

SAT
9

SUN
10   WORLD MENTAL HEALTH DAY

MON
11

TUE
12

WED
13

THU
14

FRI
15

SAT
16

SUN
17

MON
18

TUE
19

WED
20

THU
21

FRI
22

SAT
23

SUN
24

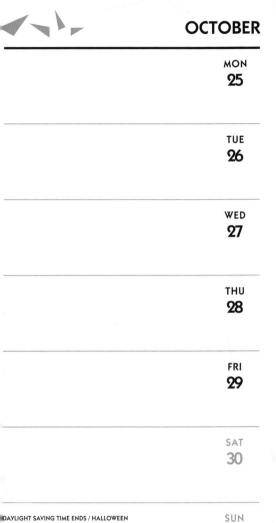

MON
25

TUE
26

WED
27

THU
28

FRI
29

SAT
30

DAYLIGHT SAVING TIME ENDS / HALLOWEEN

SUN
31

MON
1

TUE
2

WED
3

THU
4

DIWAL

FRI
5

GUY FAWKES NIGH

SAT
6

SUN
7

MON
8

___

TUE
9

___

WED
10

___

THU
11

___

FRI
12

___

SAT
13

___

SUN
14

REMEMBRANCE SUNDAY

MON
15

TUE
16

WED
17

THU
18

FRI
19

SAT
20

SUN
21

MON
22

TUE
23

WED
24

THU
25

FRI
26

SAT
27

SUN
28

MON
29

ST. ANDREW'S DAY (SCOTLAND)

TUE
30

WED
1

THU
2

FRI
3

SAT
4

SUN
5

MON
6

TUE
7

WED
8

THU
9

FRI
10

SAT
11

SUN
12

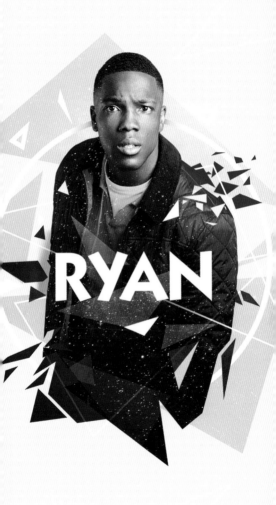

MON
13

TUE
14

WED
15

THU
16

FRI
17

SAT
18

SUN
19

MON
20

TUE
21

WED
22

THU
23

FRI
24

CHRISTMAS DAY

SAT
25

BOXING DAY

SUN
26

MON
27

BANK HOLIDAY

TUE
28

BANK HOLIDAY

WED
29

THU
30

FRI
31

NEW YEAR'S EVE

SAT
1

NEW YEAR'S DAY

SUN
2

BANK HOLIDAY

MON
3

TUE
4

WED
5

THU
6

FRI
7

SAT
8

SUN
9

CONTACTS

NAME:

....

ADDRESS:

....

....

....

....

PHONE:

....

E-MAIL:

....

NAME:

....

ADDRESS:

....

....

....

....

PHONE:

....

E-MAIL:

....

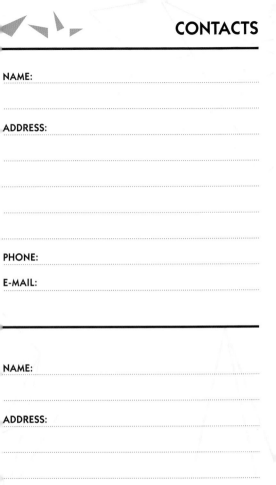

NAME:

ADDRESS:

PHONE:

E-MAIL:

NAME:

ADDRESS:

PHONE:

E-MAIL:

CONTACTS

NAME:

....

....

ADDRESS:

....

....

....

....

....

PHONE:

E-MAIL:

NAME:

....

....

ADDRESS:

....

....

....

....

....

PHONE:

E-MAIL:

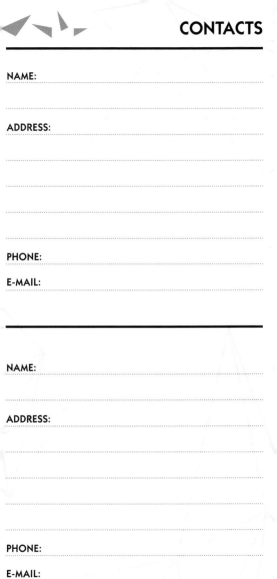

CONTACTS

NAME:

ADDRESS:

PHONE:

E-MAIL:

NAME:

ADDRESS:

PHONE:

E-MAIL:

CONTACTS

NAME:

ADDRESS:

PHONE:

E-MAIL:

NAME:

ADDRESS:

PHONE:

E-MAIL:

CONTACTS

NAME:

ADDRESS:

PHONE:

E-MAIL:

NAME:

ADDRESS:

PHONE:

E-MAIL:

CONTACTS

NAME:

ADDRESS:

PHONE:

E-MAIL:

NAME:

ADDRESS:

PHONE:

E-MAIL:

NAME:

ADDRESS:

PHONE:

E-MAIL:

NAME:

ADDRESS:

PHONE:

E-MAIL:

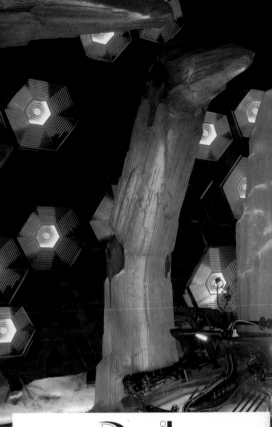

Published by Danilo Promotions Ltd. EN9 1AS, England.

Printed in South Korea.

Contact Danilo for a full listing of our complete range of Calendars, Diaries and Greeting Cards or find us on the internet:
www.danilo.com or email us at: **sales@danilo.com**

f /DaniloCalendarsUK   **✗** @CalendarsUK

While every effort is made to ensure that the information included in this diary is correct at the time of printing, Danilo Promotions Ltd. cannot be held responsible for errors and omissions. The Banking and Financial Dealings Act, 1971, allows the Government to alter dates at short notice.

Danilo is committed to making all of its products fully recyclable.